EHRET'S

Flowering Plants

THE VICTORIA AND ALBERT
NATURAL HISTORY ILLUSTRATORS

EHRET'S
Flowering Plants

HARRY N. ABRAMS, INC., PUBLISHERS

NEW YORK

INTRODUCTION

*D*rawings by Georg Dionysius Ehret (1708-70) are to be found in the collections of both the Victoria and Albert Museum and the Natural History Museum, being valued as much for their beauty of design and execution as for their interest as botanical records. His mature work was produced at a time when the foundations of botanical science were being established: Ehret himself made a major contribution, working closely with Carl Linnaeus, the Swedish scientist whose system of classification revolutionized botany and remains the basis of plant toxonomy today. It was Ehret who drew up the *tabella*, widely disseminated in printed form, which was instrumental in publicizing the Linnaean system of 'sexual characters'. The original drawing was preserved by Sir John Banks and is now in the Natural History Museum. ♣ Ehret's greatness lay in his ability to accommodate the requirements of the scientist without sacrificing the naturalism of the living specimen. Much subsequent botanical illustration subordinates realism to a schematic presentation; Ehret was able to disguise his analytical purpose in images which retain the three-dimensional vigour of a living plant. The drawings are an empirical response to the object observed and though he was largely self-taught his work is free from the artificial constraints of preconceived ideas or established formulae. His lack of formal training is evident in his depiction of the Hepatica *(Plate 28)* where the naïve rendering of the flowerpot shows that he had never learned the rules of perspective. ♣ In his brief biographical memoir Ehret

THIS MEZZOTINT PORTRAIT BY
J. J. HAID IS BASED ON AN UNFINISHED
SELF-PORTRAIT BY EHRET PAINTED
AROUND 1750. IT APPEARED IN
TREW'S 'PLANTAE SELECTAE' TO
WHICH EHRET CONTRIBUTED SOME
OF HIS FINEST DRAWINGS. HE IS
SHOWN PENCIL IN HAND, SKETCHING
A ROSE. A MORE EXOTIC SPECIMEN
AWAITS HIS ATTENTION IN A VASE
AT HIS SIDE.

LE JARDINIER FLEURISTE

attributes his rudimentary training in draughtsmanship to his father, a gardener in Heidelberg. At his father's early death Ehret was apprenticed to his uncle, also a gardener, at Bessungen near Darmstadt. He later described this period as three years of 'slavery' and continued throughout to draw plants at every opportunity. When his mother married again, to a man named Kesselbach, gardener to the Elector of Heidelberg, Georg and his brother were entrusted with the care of one of the Palatine gardens. A short period in the service of the Margrave of Baden followed but Ehret left in 1728 to pursue his career as a botanical draughtsman. His first employment in this capacity came from the apothecary Johann Wilhelm Weinmann, in Regensburg. He completed nearly 500 drawings for Weinmann's *Phytenthosa Iconographia* (1737-45) but left after a dispute over payment. This was followed by five years' work on the *Hortus Malabaricus* for the banker Loeschenkohl. During this period Ehret began his correspondence with the eminent German physician and botanist Dr. Christoph Jakob Trew (1695-1769) of Nuremburg. Favourably impressed by Ehret's drawings, Trew became his chief patron, and their association was to last until Trew's death. ♣ It was significant that Trew, as a physician, was the first to take serious note of Ehret's drawings. Since plants

THOUGH FAMOUS AS A BOTANICAL DRAUGHTSMAN EHRET SERVED HIS APPRENTICESHIP AS A GARDENER BUT HE LOATHED THE ROUTINE LABOUR OF GARDENING AND RESENTED THE 'SLAVERY' WHICH KEPT HIM FROM HIS STUDIES. HERE TENIERS SHOWS A TEAM OF GARDENERS SETTING OUT FLOWERING TREES IN POTS, A COMMON FEATURE OF THE FORMAL GARDEN.

were the major source of drugs, the development of botanical science was closely allied with the study of medicine. Accurate drawings were essential in order to identify plants, and to distinguish between species physically alike but very different in effect. Naturally there was also much interest in exotic species as the potential source of new medicines. Trew's demands were to be influential on Ehret's style and techniques. Those first drawings, of plants native to Regensburg and its environs, which brought Ehret's skills to Trew's notice, were on ordinary 'small writing paper' (320 of these are now in the collection of the Earl of Derby at Knowsley Hall). When commissioning further drawings Trew stipulated that Ehret should work on fine large sheets, representing the plants approximately life-size. He also instructed Ehret in the importance of representing the 'sexual character' of each plant in the interests of classification. Further technical improvements, such as his use of vellum in preference to paper, were prompted by a visit to the Jardin des Plantes in Paris around 1734-5. Here Ehret saw the *velins du roi*, a vast collection of vellum sheets each painted in gouache with a single example of a species. These were produced by a succession of artists appointed as *peintre du roi*, a post then held by Claude Aubriet (1665–1742), one of the great masters of flower painting. The enamel-like finish and the hard-edged precision of Aubriet's work undoubtedly influenced Ehret, though his style always remained less formal and more naturalistic. From the early 1740s he also used gouache extensively for his finished drawings, but he never entirely abandoned the transparent effects achieved with a watercolour wash. 🍀 Following his visit to France Ehret spent a year in England where he met Sir Hans Sloane, a physician and collector of plants, and Philip Miller, the curator of the Chelsea Physic Garden. Sloane was the owner of the Garden's freehold, and in 1772 had leased it to the Society of Apothecaries at £5 a year in perpetuity "on condition that it be for ever kept up and maintained by the Company as a Physic Garden". Sloane was also responsible for the appointment of Miller as Gardener in the same year. Author of the famous *Gardener's Dictionary* (1731), Miller became the greatest botanical horticulturist of his century. Peter Collinson, a fellow botanist, wrote of him:

'He has raised the reputation of the Chelsea Garden so much that it excels all the gardens of Europe for its amazing variety of plants of all orders and classes and from all climates as I survey with wonder and delight this 19th July, 1764.'

Ehret, who lodged with Miller for his first months in England, and married his sister-in-law Susanna Kennet in 1738, was thus ideally placed with an inexhaustible supply of exotic specimens close at hand. Many of his drawings were done in Chelsea Gardens and are annotated accordingly. 🍀 After a year in England Ehret travelled to Holland where he was employed by the banker George Clifford (1685-1760) to produce the 'figures' for the *Hortus Cliffortianus* (1738), a record of his garden in Haarlem. Of the thirty-four plates in the published volume, Ehret contributed twenty including the Bauhinia (*Plate 30*). The Latin text was supplied by Linnaeus, whom Ehret now met for the first time. The *Hortus Cliffortianus* was the first published work to use the new binomial system of classification, and Ehret's involvement with it consider-

ably enhanced his reputation. He returned to England in 1736 (and was to remain there for the rest of his life); his services were in constant demand amongst scholars, gardeners and plant collectors to the extent that he

often had more commissions in hand than he could fulfil. ♣ By the mid-1730s Ehret had largely abandoned his portraits of native European species. His earliest commissions from Trew had been for exotics, and subsequent patrons, such as Dr Meade, the Royal Physician, engaged him to produce paintings of rare plants and species newly introduced from the Americas, Africa and the East. England, with its colonial possessions and extensive foreign trade, saw a vast influx of exotic flowers and shrubs and became a major centre for their study and cultivation. Ehret's drawings were engraved as illustrations for travel books, notably Dr Pocock's *Description of the East* (1743-5), Dr Hughes's *History of Barbadoes* (1750), and Dr Browne's *History of Jamaica* (1756), but his finest work was published by Trew in the *Plantae Selectae*, issued in ten parts between 1750 and 1773. Trew described his plans for this work in a letter of 1742:

"Every year I receive some beautifully painted exotic plants (by Ehret) and have already more than one hundred of them, which with other pieces executed by local artists, should later on, Deo volente, constitute an appendicem to Weinmann's publication but will, I hope, find a better reception than his, for it is really regrettable that (his) precious work had so many untrue, even faked images which gave it a bad name with those who are knowledgeable....."

The emphasis was on plants recently introduced and therefore unknown to the general public. Amongst the plants illustrated here the Cereus Cactus *(Plate 34)*, the Magnolia *(Plate 29)*, the Plumeria *(Plate 33)* and the American Turkscap Lily *(Plate 16)* all appeared in the *Plantae Selectae*. ♣ Exotics feature again in *Plantae et Papiliones Rariores*, a series of plates designed and engraved by Ehret himself between 1748 and 1762. There is no consecutive text but the pages are annotated with dedications to friends and patrons, and an idiosyncratic variety of botanical information. Unlike the majority of drawings illustrated here, the plates consist not of single specimens but of an elegant arrangement of two or more plants grouped for effect rather than to denote any familial relationship. Recalling the older Herbal tradition the plants are enhanced by the addition of butterflies. These also appear in three of the paintings here (*Plates 2, 27 and 28*) but seem to have been included for compositional effect rather than scientific accuracy since the appearance of a Peacock butterfly with the winter-flowering Christmas Rose is hardly appropriate. ♣ Another of Trew's publications to which Ehret contributed was the *Hortus Nitidissimus* (1750-92), devoted to garden plants. This was essentially a florilegium, a decorative volume celebrating the beauty of plants, without any higher scientific purpose, as the sub-title explains: "The flower-garden in finest bloom throughout the year, or pictures of the most beautiful flowers". Trew did not write the text, but simply amassed the illustrations. Ehret supplied forty-four, among them the Belladonna Lily (*Plate 19*) and the Parrot Tulip (*Plate 22*), two of his showiest and most elaborate subjects. ♣ In addition to the humble native flora and the flamboyant exotica Ehret drew many varieties of the so-called 'florist's flowers' which, in the eighteenth century, were obsessively cultivated to conform to rigorous standards of perfection. Seven flowers predominated – the carnation, tulip, auricula, anemone, hyacinth, ranunculus and narcissus. The tulip, with its unpredictable habit of 'breaking' into striped or variegated forms (*Plate 23*)

THOUGH PUBLISHED IN 1742, AND

THEREFORE CONTEMPORARY

WITH EHRET'S FINEST WORK, THE

'RECEUIL DE FLEURS' IS CLOSER

IN STYLE AND SPIRIT TO THE

FLORILEGIA OF THE PRECEDING

CENTURY.

inspired an excessive passion amongst gardeners. At the height of this 'Tulipomania' in the seventeenth century, bulbs changed hands for phenomenal prices and it remained expensive and highly prized well into the following century. The auricula, an alpine, reached the height of its popularity in the eighteenth century and Ehret himself seems to have had a particular affection for this dainty plant, painting many examples. We do not know who commissioned these portraits; they seem not to have been engraved for published works. Possibly they record prize-winning specimens at the newly established flower shows, or perhaps Ehret painted them for his own pleasure. Though as finely executed as any of his exotic subjects, they are often un-captioned or inscribed simply with the plant's common name. ♣ Though its chief publicist, Ehret's use of the binomial system (in which each plant was allotted two names, one to indicate genus, another for species) was often erratic. Many plates have instead lengthy descriptions in Latin. Ehret did, however, annotate many of his drawings with fascinating details. He usually dated his work and often noted the garden in which he saw the plant and the publication for which it was intended. According to the inscription accompanying the Turkscap Lily (Plate 16) "this lily first flowered in the month of August 1738 in the curious garden of Peter Collinson" and Ehret recorded it there. Such inscriptions are valuable in tracing the history of non-native species and also reveal Ehret's diligence in seeking out new specimens. In August 1737, for instance, he walked daily the three miles from Chelsea to Parsons Green to study the opening buds of *Magnolia grandiflora* in the garden of Sir Charles Wager. 🌿 A stylistic development is apparent in Ehret's drawings. The work of the 1730s is highly decorative, the specimen presented in an elegant but artificial manner as with the Cistus *(Plate 12)* where three cuttings are tied together by a 'rococo' ribbon. By the 1740s he had abandoned this formal manner for the vigorous realistic images which made him famous. Wherever possible he liked to show the plant growing, solidly rooted in the soil (though this may be cut away to show the bulb, as in *Plate 18*). Many of the exotics, however, are presented as cuttings, which suggest that he was working from dried and mounted herbarium specimens sent from abroad and had not studied the living plant. They are nevertheless as convincing as those drawn from life. Ehret's drawings have been justly described as portraits, for they offer a close and accurate likeness of their subjects. With the rare exception of the drooping rose *(Plate 3)* with its damaged leaves his plants are flawless examples of their kind. Like a painter of human portraits he improves upon nature, smoothing out the imperfections and showing his subjects at their best.

THE PLATES

Plate 1

Plate 2

HELLEBORUS niger, flore albo, etiam interdum valde rubente. 43.
True Black Hellebore, or Christmas rose.

Plate 3

Rosa Provincialis spinosissima, pedunculo muscoso Cat. Hort.

Plate 4

The Royal Virgin Rose without Thorns.

Plate 5

Plate 6

Plate 7

Plate 8

Plate 9

Plate 10

The deep purple Lilac.

Plate 11

Plate 12

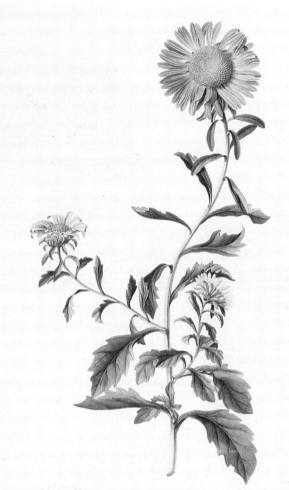

ASTER annuus, caule villoso purpurascente, Eryngii folio,
flore maximo purpureo pulcherrimo, semine violaceo. *Infusion*

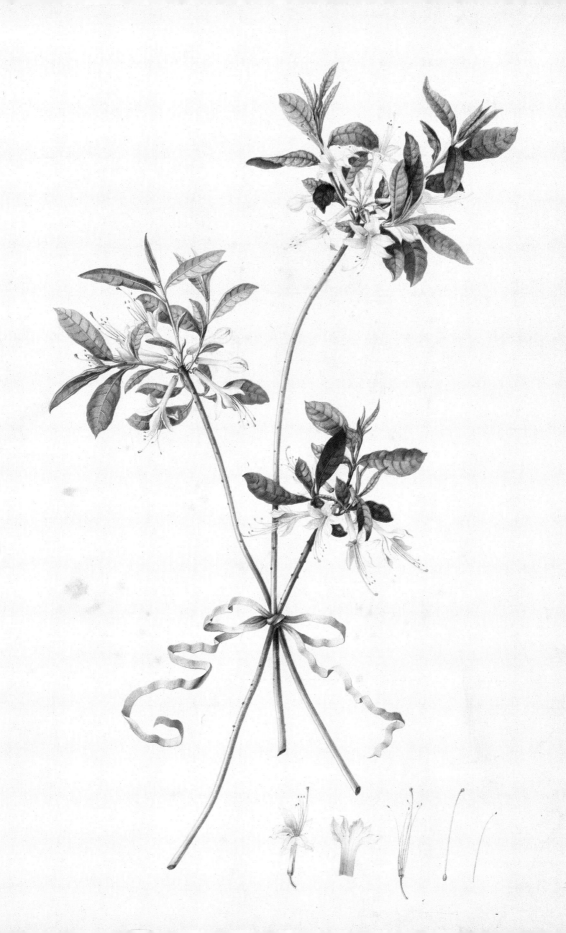

Plate 13

Plate 14

BIGNONIA *Americana, fraxini folie, flore ample phœnicie* Tourn

Plate 15

Plate 16

LILIVM *folus sparsis*
floribus reflexis pedunculo
floris and folio notato (prius)

Plate 17

LILIO-NARCISSUS *facetans, flore sanguineo nutante*

Plate 18

LILIO-NARCISSVS, indicus, flore albo,
exterius rubente. Tom. iç.

G. D. Ehret. pinx.

Plate 19

LILIO NARCISSUS Americanus Belladona dictus.

Plate 20

Plate 21

Plate 22

Veld haan.

Perroquet rouge.

Plate 23

Plate 24

Duke of Cumberland

Plate 25

Fille Amoureuse

G. D. Ehret pinxerunt

Plate 26

AURICULA-URSI *Virginiana, floribus albis Borraginis instar rostratis. Cyclaminum more reflexis.* D. Banist. Rai. Hist. 1.6 pl 16

Plate 27

Plate 28

HEPATICA *trifolia flore rubro pleno.* Beera *fad.*

Plate 29

MAGNOLIA *altissima Lauro-Cerasi folio flore ingenti candide* Catesb.
The Laurel-leaved Tulip-tree.

Plate 30

Bauhinia foliis quinquenerviis lobis acuminatis remotissimis. Linn. Amœn. Coff.

Plate 33

PLUMERIA flore roseo odoratissimo. pp. R.S.

Plate 34

CEREUS *scandens minor*
polygonus articulatus. ...

Plate 35

Plate 36

IASMINUM Arabicum Castanea folio flore albo,
odoratißimo cujus fructus Coffy in officinis dicuntur nobis.
The Coffee tree.

Plate 37

Plate 38

Plate 39

CEDRUS magna fire Libani, unifera.

Plate 40

LIST OF PLATES